BOOK FOUR

D0896694

·✦·THE TWILIGHT OF THE GODS·✦·

Adapted by Roy Thomas ▫ Art by Gil Kane

Color Art by Jim Woodring ▫ Lettered by John Costanza

NAY--THAT IS ONLY THE CAPTIVE WRITHINGS OF *LOGE* THE FIRE-GOD.

IT STILL IS *NIGHT.*

LET US *SPIN*-- AND *SING* WHILE WE SPIN!

YES...

AWAKE, MY SISTER NORNS!

WHAT *LIGHT* BURNS THERE, ON THE ROCK WHERE ONCE A *VALKYRIE* SLEPT?

DOES THE *DAY* ALREADY DAWN?

FOR WELL, OR FOR ILL-- I SING OF *THINGS THAT WERE,* AND THINGS *THAT WILL BE*--

--AND I *WIND* THE ROPE.

ONCE, I *WOVE* AT THE *WORLD-ASH TREE,* WHEN FROM ITS HUGE TRUNK GREW THE BOUGHS OF A *SACRED FOREST.*

IN THE GREAT TREE'S SHADOW BUBBLED THE WELL OF WISDOM.

WOTAN, KING OF GODS, CAME ONE DAY TO DRINK AT IT...

...DESPERATE TO GAIN THE *KNOW-LEDGE OF THINGS TO COME!*

ONE I KNOW OF-- NONE *NOBLER* IN ALL THE WORLD!

FAIR *BRÜNNHILDE* DWELLS ON SOARING ROCKS, ENCIRCLED BY FIRE.

HE WHO'D WIN HER MUST BREAK THROUGH THAT FLAME.

AND YOU THINK *MY* STRENGTH IS SUFFICIENT FOR THAT TASK?

ALAS, GUNTHER, THAT DEED IS RESERVED FOR THE *VOLSUNG*, *SIEGFRIED*--HE WHO SLEW A DRAGON TO WIN THE *GOLD OF THE NIBELUNG.*

WHAT? THEY SAY THAT TREASURE HOARD IS *PRICELESS!*

AYE! THE MAN WHO COULD *USE* ITS SPELL--WERE *LORD OF THE WORLD,* FOREVER-MORE!

SIEGMUND AND SIEGLINDA-- A TWIN-BORN PAIR WHOM FATE TURNED TO LOVERS-- WERE HIS STAR-CROSSED PARENTS...

...AND 'TIS HE THAT *YOU* SHOULD WED, DEAR *GUTRINE!*

I? YOU *MOCK* ME, HAGEN!

WHAT ARTS HAVE *I* TO WIN THE GREATEST HERO IN ALL THE WORLD?

REMEMBER THE *HERB-POTION* LOCKED AWAY IN YOUR JEWEL-CHEST, MY LADY?

IF SIEGFRIED DRANK OF IT, HE'D *FORGET* ANY WOMAN HE'D EVER SEEN BEFORE!

THEN, GUNTHER, WITH HIS HEART A PRISONER TO OUR SISTER, YOU'VE ONLY TO *ASK* HIM--

--AND HE WILL *GLADLY* GO WIN YOUR FIRE-HEMMED *BRIDE* FOR YOU!

WELL? WHAT DO YOU THINK OF MY PLAN?

MAY OUR MOTHER BE PRAISED, WHO GAVE US YOU FOR A HALF-BROTHER!

I MUST *SEE* THIS SIEGFRIED!

BUT HOW CAN HE BE FOUND, HAGEN?

WHICH OF YOU IS GUNTHER, SON OF GIBICH?

I AM THE ONE YOU SEEK.

YOUR FAME HAS REACHED ME FAR OFF ALONG THE RHINE...

NOW *FIGHT* WITH ME--OR ELSE BE MY *FRIEND.*

FRIEND, THEN! YOU ARE WELCOME HERE.

I AM GLAD. BUT--HOW DID YOUR MAN KNOW MY NAME?

I GUESSED FROM WHO YOU MUST BE...FROM YOUR NOBLE BEARING.

COME INSIDE, AND GREET MY FATHER'S HALL IN GLADNESS.

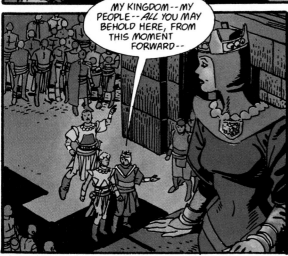

MY KINGDOM--MY PEOPLE--*ALL* YOU MAY BEHOLD HERE, FROM THIS MOMENT FORWARD--

--TREAT AS YOUR OWN!

MY *SWORD* AND *MYSELF* DO I OFFER, IN RETURN.

FOR MY OWN *BODY* IS ALL MY WEALTH I HAVE TO GIVE-- AND, AS I LIVE, IT GROWS EVER LESS.

OH? YET, RUMORS NAME YOU LORD OF THE *NIBELUNG DWARF'S TREASURE.*

THE HOARD? I ALMOST FORGOT ABOUT IT --

-- SO LIGHTLY DO I PRIZE ITS WORTH.

I LEFT IT LYING IN A CAVERN, WHERE A DRAGON ONCE STOOD WATCH.

AND YOU TOOK NOTHING AT ALL FROM SUCH A TREASURE?

ONLY...ONE THING...

...THIS *HELMET,* WHOSE VALUE I DO NOT EVEN KNOW.

WHY, 'TIS THE LEGENDARY *TARNHELM* --

-- THE CROWNING GEM OF THE NIBELUNG'S ART!

WORN ON YOUR HEAD, IT WILL *CHANGE YOUR SHAPE* TO WHATEVER YOU WILL!

IF YOU WISH TO BE *BORNE AFAR*-- IN A FLASH, *LO!* YOU WILL BE THERE!

AND YOU TOOK... *NOTHING* ELSE?

WELL... THERE WAS A *RING*.

AND YOU'RE-- KEEPING IT *SAFE?*

A WOMAN MOST WONDEROUS IS.

NAY, SIEGFRIED, LET US NOT BARTER.

ALL I HAVE IS BUT A POOR BAUBLE, MATCHED AGAINST YOUR TREASURE.

I WILL SERVE YOU GLADLY, WITH-OUT HOPE OF REWARD.

WELCOME, O GUEST, TO *GIBICH'S HOUSE.*

'TIS HIS *DAUGHTER* GIVES YOU TO DRINK.

IF ALL WERE *FORGOTTEN* THAT YOU TOLD ME, ONE LESSON I WOULD *NEVER* FORGET.

AND SO THIS FIRST DRAUGHT-- WITH *LOVE UNDYING*--

--*BRÜNNHILDE,* I DRINK TO THEE!

THEN LET THE *BLOOD-OATH* NOW BE *SWORN!*

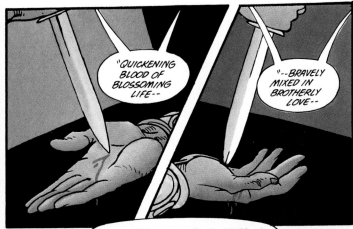

"*QUICKENING BLOOD OF BLOSSOMING LIFE--*

"*--BRAVELY MIXED IN BROTHERLY LOVE--*

"*--IF BROKEN THIS BOND, OR FAITH-LESS THE FRIEND--LET HE WHO BREAKS IT PAY THE WAGE OF TREACHERY!*"

SEALED BE OUR BOND!

PLEDGED BE OUR FAITH!

HAGEN, WHY DID *YOU* NOT JOIN IN THE OATH?

MY BLOOD IS NOT SO *PURE* OR *NOBLE* AS YOURS.

SO I HOLD *ALOOF* FROM HOT-BLOODED BONDS.

LET THAT UNHAPPY CHURL BE, SIEGFRIED.

WILL YOU REST A WHILE, BEFORE WE BEGIN OUR QUEST?

NO. I AM EAGER THAT WE SHOULD DEPART--

--THE SOONER THAT I MAY RETURN TO GUTRUNE.

I...?

...GUNTHER...?

YOU ARE LYING!

THE LIGHT... FADES FROM MY EYES...

SIEGFRIED-- DON'T YOU KNOW ME?

GUNTHER--

YOUR BRIDE IS SWOONING!

WAKE, BRÜNNHILDE...

HERE STANDS YOUR HUSBAND.

THE... RING...

...THE RING UPON HIS HAND...

HE...

...SIEGFRIED?

HAVE YOU A TALE TO TELL US, MY LADY?

--I, WHOM LOVE HAS TRULY BLESSED WITH VIRTUOUS *GUTRUNE!*

WHAT *WIZARD'S SPELL* HAS WORKED THIS WOE?

I GAVE SIEGFRIED ALL MY *RUNE-WISDOM,* AND NOW I AM MERELY HIS *BOOTY*-- TO BE LIGHTLY GIVEN TO ANOTHER!

WILL NO ONE LEND A *SWORD* WITH WHICH I MAY SEVER MY *UN-SEEN BONDS?*

LEAVE THAT TO *HAGEN,* WRONGED ONE.

I WILL AVENGE YOU ON SIEGFRIED!

YOU?

A SINGLE FLASH OF HIS *EYE* AND ITS *LIGHTNING*-- AND YOUR COURAGE WOULD DESERT YOU!

BUT HIS *OATH-LIES...* THEY MAKE HIM VULNERABLE TO MY *SPEAR!*

TRUTH -- FALSEHOOD-- WHAT MATTER MERE WORDS?

SEEK FOR SOME-THING *STRONGER,* IF YOU WOULD WITH-STAND SUCH POWER AS HIS!

I KNOW WELL OF SIEGFRIED'S PROWESS IN BATTLE.

THEN WHISPER TO ME SOME *SECRET WAY* TO SPEED HIM TO HIS DOOM!

I TAUGHT HIM ALL THE RUNIC ARTS I KNOW TO PRESERVE HIS BODY FROM HARM.

WITHOUT HIS KNOWING IT, HE BEARS A *CHARMED LIFE,* AND WALKS ALL WRAPPED ABOUT WITH PROTECTING *SPELLS.*

THEN-- *NO* WEAPON FORGED COULD HARM HIM?

... THE BRIDAL PROCESSION COMES...

THE DIE IS CAST!

SIEGFRIED'S FATE IS SEALED.

MINE WILL BE BOTH RING AND HOARD OF GOLD-- AND MINE SHALL I HOLD IT!

FATHER-- ALBERICH-- HEAR YOUR SON!

BID THE NIBELUNG HOST OBEY YOU ONCE AGAIN --

--THE RING'S DREAD LORD!

THOUGH THE *SUN* SENDS OUT ITS RAYS OF GLORY...

...HERE IN THE *RHINE* THERE IS ONLY *DARKNESS...!*

O SUN -- SEND US THE *HERO* WHO SHALL GIVE BACK TO US OUR STOLEN *GOLD!*

RHINEGOLD -- HOW BRIGHT ONCE WAS YOUR RADIANCE --

-- GLORIOUS STAR OF THE WATERS!

HOLD, SISTERS! HE COMES!

SIEGFRIED!

HO, DOWN THERE, FROLICKSOME MAIDS!

HAVE YOU SEEN THE SHAGGY - HIDED *BEAST* I WAS PURSUING?

WHAT WILL YOU GIVE US IF WE TELL YOU?

I HAVE CAUGHT NOTHING YET, SO ASK WHAT YOU WILL.

AH! THAT TASTED GOOD!

YOU ARE QUIET TODAY, GUNTHER.

HERE -- DRINK! YOUR BLOOD-BROTHER OFFERS YOU THE HORN.

A...PALE WINE YOU HAVE POURED... *BROTHER*...

...WITH NO BLOOD BUT *YOURS* IN IT!

POOR, SAD GUNTHER.

PERHAPS A TALE OF MY *BOYHOOD* WILL CHEER UP WHAT BRÜNNHILDE HAS MARRED.

OUT OF GREED, A SURLY OLD DWARF NAMED *MIME* REARED ME, SO I COULD SLAY A *DRAGON* FOR HIM WHEN I GREW UP.

HE TAUGHT ME TO FORGE, AND FROM THE SPLINTERS OF MY FATHER'S BLADE I FASHIONED MY OWN SWORD, *"NEEDFUL."*

IN THE FOREST, I SLEW THE DRAGON *FAFNER*, WHO GUARDED THE NIBELUNG GOLD.

BUT WHEN I TOUCHED ITS *BLOOD* TO MY LIPS, I HEARD A *BIRD* SPEAKING OF THE *TARNHELM* --

--AND OF THE *RING* WHICH COULD MAKE ME *LORD OF THE WORLD.*

WHEN I HAD OBTAINED BOTH, THAT SAME BIRD WARNED ME THAT *MIME* WAS NOW BENT ON *MURDERING* ME, FOR THE SAKE OF THE *GOLD.*

THE DWARF TRIED TO *POISON* ME WITH A DEADLY BREW --

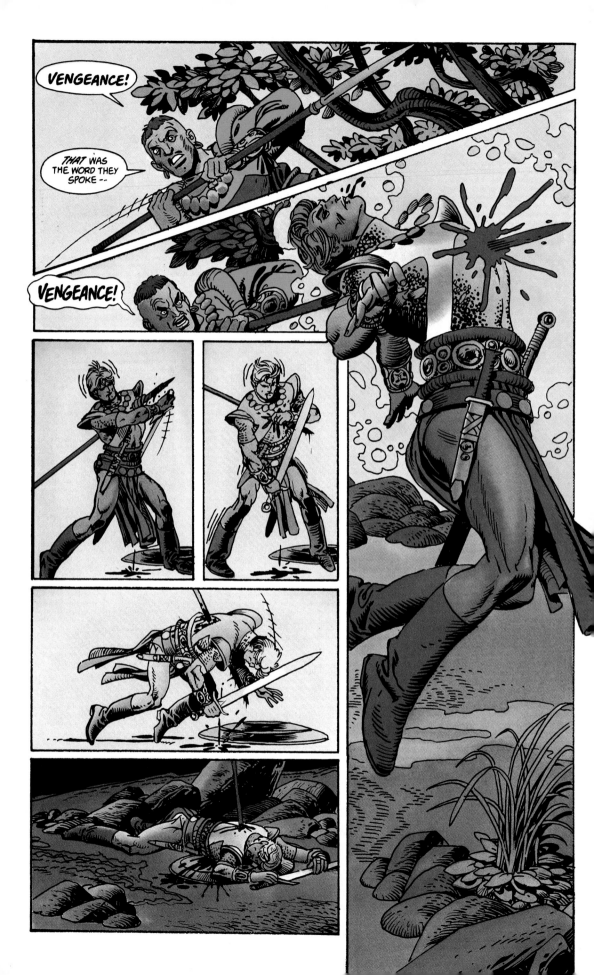

HAGEN-- WHAT HAVE YOU DONE?

I HAVE BUT BROUGHT *DEATH*, DEAR GUNTHER--

--TO A *BREAKER OF OATHS!*

BRÜNNHILDE...

MY...

...BRIDE...

WAS THAT *BRÜNNHILDE* I SAW GO DOWN- WARD TO THE *RHINE*?

OH, WHEN WILL *SIEGFRIED* RETURN?

HAGEN? WHAT IS WRONG?

I SAW THE *TORCHES*, BUT-- WHAT ARE THEY CARRYING?

A *WILD BOAR'S PREY* THEY BRING TO YOU, GENTLE SISTER--

-- YOUR HUSBAND *SIEGFRIED*--

--SLAIN!

SIEGFRIED...?

YOU! FALSE-HEARTED BROTHER-- MURDERER OF MY HUSBAND!

NO! HAGEN IS THE ACCURSED "WILD BOAR" WHO DEALT THE HERO'S DEATH!

AND YOU REVILE ME FOR IT, NOW?

THEY HAVE SLAIN SIEGFRIED?

THEN-- YES! I SLEW HIM WITH THE SPEAR BY WHICH HE FALSELY SWORE.

AND FOR MY PRIZE, I CLAIM-- THE RING!

AWAY! YOU'LL NOT HAVE WHAT RIGHTLY FALLS TO ME, NIBELUNG-SON!

I WILL SHOW YOU HOW THE SON OF THE NIBELUNG DEMANDS HIS OWN!

THE RING IS MINE!

MINE!

SILENCE YOUR CLAMORING!

NOW, FOR HER VENGEANCE, SIEGFRIED'S TRUE WIFE COMES--

--THE WOMAN ALL HAVE BETRAYED!

NEVER DID MAN SWEAR OATHS MORE HONEST...NEVER WAS LOVE MORE PURE THAN HIS...

YET NEVER WAS OATH OR LOVE SO GROSSLY *BETRAYED!*

WOTAN, YOU WHO GUARD ALL VOWS--LOOK DOWN AND BEHOLD YOUR *ETERNAL GUILT!*

THROUGH SIEGFRIED'S VALIANT DEED-- A DEED BY YOU *DESIRED* --YOU DID CONDEMN HIM TO THE *DOOM* THAT ELSE HAD FALLEN ON THE *GODS!*

I KNOW *ALL THINGS* NOW-- AND I CLAIM AS MINE WHAT HE HAS LEFT ME--

--THIS *RING ACCURST!*

THE *RHINE-MAIDENS* SHALL HAVE IT AT LAST, FROM OUT OF MY ASHES.

THE VERY *FIRE* WHICH CONSUMES ME *CLEANSES* THE RING OF ITS CURSE!

LET THEM *GUARD* FOREVER THE SHINING GOLD THAT WAS STOLEN FROM THEM!

YOU RAVENS-- GO TELL YOUR LORD WHAT YOU HAVE SEEN AND HEARD BY THE RHINE!

BUT AS YOU GO, FLY BY *BRÜNN-HILDE'S ROCK*--

--AND BID *LOGE* FOLLOW YOU BACK HOME--

--FOR THE GODS ARE DRAWING NEAR THEIR DOOM!

THUS IS THE FIREBRAND HURLED UPON *VALHALLA'S* GLITTERING WALLS, AS WELL!

GRANE-- DO THE LAUGHING FLAMES DRAW YOU TO FOLLOW YOUR MASTER?

AH, TO BE EMBRACED BY *SIEGFRIED*-- UNITED FOREVER IN LOVE WITHOUT END!

HEIAJOHO, GRANE--

-- GIVE YOUR LORD *GREETING!*

...THE NIBELUNG RING SHALL RESIDE IN ITS RIGHTFUL PLACE...

...AT THE BOTTOM OF THE RIVER RHINE.

THEN, AS THE WATERS RETIRE TO THEIR NATURAL BED AT LAST...

...THERE SHALL BE SEEN A GROWING GLEAM OF FIRE IN THE HEAVENS...

...AND THOSE WHO HAVE EYES TO SEE SHALL WITNESS FROM AFAR...